Dracula

Dracula

**Based on the classic novel
by Bram Stoker**

SCHOLASTIC INC.
New York Toronto London Auckland Sydney
Mexico City New Delhi Hong Kong Buenos Aires

Cover and interior photographs from
***Dracula*, Universal Pictures, 1931,**
Museum of Modern Art Film Stills Archive

Characters

Narrator 1

Narrator 2

Jonathan Harker, a young lawyer

Harker's diary

Count Dracula

Mina Murray, Jonathan Harker's fiancée

Mina's journal

Dr. John Seward, a doctor at a mental hospital

Seward's journal

Mr. Renfield, a mental patient

Professor Van Helsing, a doctor from Amsterdam

Van Helsing's journal

Nurse

Attendant, a worker at the hospital

Newspaper article

Introduction

Narrator 1: Here is a story of terrible horror. And all of it is true. So, reader, beware! Yes, here is a world of undead souls who live on blood. And, dear reader, it is the same world you walk in today!

Narrator 2: Our story begins in 1897, in Transylvania, a region of eastern Europe. Jonathan Harker is a young English lawyer. He is sent to Transylvania on business. The mysterious Count Dracula wants to buy a house in England. Harker will be handling the paperwork. During his trip, Harker keeps a diary. It will help tell the story.

"Welcome to my house. I am Dracula." In 1931, actor Bela Lugosi starred as the Transylvanian vampire in the film *Dracula.* It became one of the most famous horror movies ever.

Scene 1   **Transylvania**

Harker's diary: I was driven to Castle Dracula in a coach. It was very late at night. It was so dark that I could hardly see. When I told people where I was going, they were very scared. They repeated a strange word. It sounded like "wampire." Were they trying to warn me of something?

Narrator 1: Harker arrives at the dark castle. A strange man greets him.

Harker's diary: A tall, old man with very pale skin stood there. He was dressed in black. And he wore a cape. He waved me inside, and he spoke with an odd accent.

Count Dracula: Welcome to my house! Enter free. Leave safe. But leave a taste of happiness when you go.

Harker's diary: Count Dracula shook my hand and almost crushed it. Worse still, his hand was cold as ice, like a dead person's. I shivered.

Jonathan Harker: I'm here to see Count Dracula.

Dracula: I am Dracula. Come in. The night air will give you a chill. You must need to eat and rest.

Harker's diary: He led me through many dark halls and up many stairs. Finally, he opened the door to a dining room.

Dracula: Please be seated and dine. Excuse me now. I will not join you. I have dined already.

Harker's diary: After dinner, we sat by a fire in the Count's den. I was telling him about Carfax, the house he is buying in England. Suddenly, I heard a terrible sound outside. It was the howling of a pack of wolves. I looked at the Count. He just smiled at me.

Dracula: Listen to them. They are the children of the night. What music they make!

Harker's diary: He saw that I was afraid.

Dracula: Ah, sir. You city people cannot understand the feelings of the hunter. Come, you must be tired. Your bedroom is waiting. Sleep as long as you like. I will be away until tomorrow night.

Why do you think Count Dracula doesn't join Harker for dinner?

Scene 2

Narrator 2: The next day, Harker sleeps until late afternoon.

Harker's diary: I found myself alone in the huge castle. I wanted to shave. But I could not find a mirror anywhere. Finally, I remembered I had a small mirror in my shaving kit. I took it out and started to shave.

Narrator 1: Suddenly, Harker senses someone behind him. He turns to find the Count staring at him.

Harker's diary: For some reason, I did not see the Count in my mirror. He startled me. I cut my chin with my razor. A few drops of blood trickled out.

Bela Lugosi was born in Hungary. His thick accent was perfect for the role of Dracula. *"I vant to sock your blud!"* he frighteningly—and famously—told his victims.

Narrator 2: The Count sees the blood. His eyes flash. He lunges at Harker. And his hand reaches for Harker's throat.

Harker's diary: I jumped back. Dracula's hand touched the rosary that I wear around my neck. That seemed to change his mood. He removed his icy hands from my skin.

Dracula: Take care not to cut yourself. It is more dangerous than you think.

Narrator 1: Then the Count vanishes as quietly as he had arrived.

Harker's diary: What kind of man is my host? Where does he go all day? Why doesn't he eat with me? Why did he grab my neck? And why didn't I see him in my mirror?

Narrator 2: Harker decides to search the castle.

Harker's diary: All I found was a maze of doors, doors, doors everywhere. And every one of them was locked and bolted. This castle has become a prison. And I fear that I am its prisoner!

Scene 3

Narrator 1: Harker sits alone in his room. Late that night, he sees something strange. A beautiful woman in a long dress appears before him.

Harker's diary: I wasn't sure if I was awake or dreaming. She kept coming closer to me. When she was just inches away, I saw her sharp teeth. I was trapped. She leaned toward my throat. I felt her breath on my skin.

Narrator 2: Suddenly, a wolf appears from nowhere. It changes into Count Dracula. Blood covers the Count's lips, and his eyes are filled with anger. He starts to scream at the woman.

Dracula: How dare you touch him! I warned you to stay away! This man belongs to me. You are welcome to him in a month. I will be finished with him then. If I catch you in here again, you will pay. Now away!

Narrator 1: Dracula turns to Harker, who is shaking with fear.

Dracula: Try to forget that little disturbance, my friend. And do not worry. I need you alive to sell me that property. After that, of course, who knows?

Harker's diary: Now it is all clear to me. Dracula is a vampire! That's why he did not show up in my mirror! He is an undead creature of the night. He drinks the blood of living humans. I do not know why he wants to buy the Carfax house in England. But it will take a month to complete the sale. And he needs my signature. Then, either Dracula or that woman will drink my blood—unless I escape!

Scene 4 England

Narrator 2: At the same time, Mina Murray arrives in the town of Whitby on the English seashore. She is engaged to marry Jonathan Harker.

Mina's journal: I'm so glad to be back where I grew up. Just think, a whole summer here in paradise. But there's still no word from my poor Jonathan. His company received a note from Count Dracula in Transylvania. The Count says he needs Jonathan's help for another month. I can't stop worrying about him.

Narrator 1: The next day, Mina visits her friend Dr. Seward. He runs a mental hospital. His house is on the hospital grounds.

Dr. John Seward: It's lovely to see you again, Mina. Just the other day I was thinking about when you were a child. Remember? You were so easily frightened. You used to think that Carfax, that estate next door, was haunted.

Mina Murray: Oh, John, I was so young and silly.

Seward: Of course. Well, I hear that Carfax has been sold at last. I can't imagine who would buy that old place.

Narrator 2: As Dr. Seward talks, a huge man with wild eyes creeps into the room. Mina watches him as he stands, chuckling to himself. Dr. Seward turns and sees him.

Seward: Mr. Renfield, you know better than to come in here! *(to Mina)* Please forgive this gentleman. He is one of my patients, Mr. Renfield.

Narrator 1: Dr. Seward calls for a hospital attendant.

Attendant: Sorry, Dr. Seward. I don't know how he got out of his room.

Narrator 2: As Dr. Seward and the attendant talk, Renfield creeps to the window. He watches a fly on the sill. Suddenly, he snatches it and pops it into his mouth.

Seward: Mr. Renfield, stop that! You are not to eat any more creatures—not even flies or spiders.

Mr. Renfield: But they're really very tasty and nutritious, Dr. Seward. They give me life. I feed ten flies to a spider, then I eat the spider. It gives me such power. It's eleven lives all in one!

Narrator 1: The attendant drags Renfield back to his room.

How is the patient Mr. Renfield similar to Count Dracula?

Scene 5

Narrator 2: A few days later, the local newspaper reports an eerie event. The whole town is alarmed.

Newspaper article: "Ghost Ship Runs Aground." A strange ship crashed on the shore during the storm last night. A dead man was tied to the ship's wheel. He was the only human found aboard. A witness said that a giant dog jumped from the deck and ran off into the night. The ship's only cargo was 50 large boxes of dirt. These boxes are addressed for delivery to the Carfax estate.

Narrator 1: Of course, no one knows that the "dog" from the ship is actually Count Dracula in the shape of a wolf.

Dracula inspects his coffins. A Spanish version of *Dracula* was made at the same time as Lugosi's *Dracula*. The Spanish one was shot at night, using the same sets and different actors.

Narrator 2: Later that day, Dr. Seward writes in his journal.

Seward's journal: I'm worried about Mina. Last night, during the storm, her maid found her sleepwalking. She was headed for the window, with her arms stretched out.

Mr. Renfield was very odd last night, too. He kept shouting, "He's here! The master is here!"

Could all this strange behavior have anything to do with the ghost ship?

Why do you think Mina was sleepwalking during the storm?

Scene 6

Narrator 2: A month passes, and Mina becomes very sick. She cannot get out of bed. Dr. Seward examines her and writes about her in his journal.

Seward's journal: The patient is very pale and weak. She has lost a lot of blood. But how? There is no bleeding. The only marks on her body are two tiny holes, like pinpricks, on her neck.

Narrator 1: Over the next few days, Mina's condition grows worse.

Seward's journal: I have sent for my teacher from medical school, Professor Van Helsing of Amsterdam.

Narrator 2: Professor Van Helsing arrives and examines Mina. Alarmed, he calls Dr. Seward into the next room.

Professor Van Helsing: You were right to call me. I know exactly what's wrong with the young woman.

Seward: What a relief! What is it?

Van Helsing: She is the victim of a vampire.

Seward: A vampire? Are you insane? With all due respect, Professor, there must be some other explanation. Vampires don't exist!

Van Helsing: Young man, there are many things on this earth that we cannot explain. You must open your mind. You must believe in this vampire, or there is no hope for Mina.

Seward: I will if I can. What kind of creature are you talking about?

Van Helsing: Vampires are persons who exist somewhere between life and death. They have been robbed of their souls. The only way they can live is to drink the blood of innocent people. They bite into their victims' throats.

Seward: Then those spots on Mina's neck are teeth marks! The vampire is killing her!

Van Helsing: It may be worse than that. Some of a vampire's victims do not die. They themselves become vampires! And they must begin drinking the blood of others.

Seward: But how could this happen to Mina?

Van Helsing: Vampires can do almost anything they want. They can turn themselves into bats or wolves or mist. They can hypnotize their victims. Vampires can even control people who are asleep. It's possible that Mina herself doesn't know what's happening to her.

Seward: How can we stop this monster?

Van Helsing: Vampires sleep in their coffins during the day. They only wake to do their evil deeds once the sun goes down. So we will only need to watch Mina at night. I know of several things that will protect her from the vampire. We will try garlic bulbs.

Seward: But we can't protect her forever.

Van Helsing: You're right. We must kill the vampire. There's only one way to do it: We must drive a wooden stake through his heart. Only then will he rest.

Seward: I have one more question, Professor Van Helsing. Do you think that Mina has become a vampire?

Van Helsing: Not yet. But if this vampire takes too much of her blood, her soul will leave. Then all is lost.

How does Professor Van Helsing know that Mina is the victim of a vampire?

Scene 7

Van Helsing's journal: Tonight we lined the windows and doors of Mina's room with garlic bulbs. They smelled terrible, but maybe they will work. I made a ring of them for the girl to wear around her neck. This should keep her safe during the night.

Narrator 1: A few hours later, the doctors return to check on Mina. They discover that a nurse has moved all the garlic bulbs into the hall.

Nurse: When I checked on Miss Mina, a huge bat was pounding against the window. He scared me. I thought maybe he was attracted to the garlic, so I took it all away.

Van Helsing: Dr. Seward, prepare yourself for whatever we may find in there!

Narrator 2: They burst into the room. A tall, old man is bending over Mina. When he lifts his head, blood trickles down his chin.

Dracula: Good evening, gentlemen. Allow me to introduce myself. I am Count Dracula. I'll forgive you this one time. But let me warn you. Do not try again to stop me. You are no match for my powers. My own country is running out of souls. But your land is full of life. I intend to make these souls mine!

Seward: Old man, leave that woman alone!

Dracula: Silence, fool! You try my patience. I am talking about things too large for your tiny mind. Speak to me no more!

Seward's journal: What happened next was so fast, I almost didn't see it. Dracula flew at Van Helsing like a giant bat. The professor then pulled out a gold cross and held it in front of him. This seemed to scare the creature. He turned into a mist and then floated out of the room through a crack under the door.

Professor Van Helsing, played by an actor named Edward Van Sloan. Both Lugosi and Van Sloan appeared in a Broadway play about Dracula before the movie was made.

Scene 8

Narrator 1: The doctors are able to help Mina. Other victims that night are not so lucky. An old couple in town is found dead. No blood is left in their bodies. Professor Van Helsing realizes that the entire town is in danger. He knows that he and Dr. Seward must kill Dracula. But first they must find the vampire's resting place.

Narrator 2: Late the next day, Dr. Seward and Professor Van Helsing sit in Dr. Seward's office. They are tired and worried. They discuss ways to protect Mina and the village. The attendant knocks on the door.

Attendant: Sorry to disturb you, but there is a man here to see you. His name is Jonathan Harker. He is a friend of Miss Mina Murray.

Narrator 1: Dr. Seward and Professor Van Helsing meet Harker in the hallway. He has grown very thin and pale.

Harker: Sirs, I have been away on a terrible journey. I was trapped in a horrible place. I barely managed to escape. Now I have returned to look for my fiancée. I heard that she is ill. What is wrong with her?

Van Helsing: You would not believe us if we told you. But let me ask: Does the name *Dracula* mean anything to you?

Narrator 2: A look of terror crosses Harker's face. Then he faints. A few minutes later, he wakes up.

Harker: I know the vampire Dracula very well. It was from his castle that I escaped. I climbed out a window as he slept. That night, I hid in the forest. I was shaking with fear. I could hear his terrible cries as he hunted for me.

Seward: How horrible! But why is he here?

Harker: He just bought the Carfax estate!

Scene 9

Narrator 1: Later, as the sun sets, Dr. Seward, Professor Van Helsing, and Harker sneak into the Carfax estate. They creep slowly down the cellar stairs. As they reach the bottom, they see a large wooden box—Dracula's coffin—in the middle of the floor.

Harker: That's it. Be careful. He's very clever.

Narrator 2: They slowly open the lid of the coffin.

Van Helsing: There lies the monster, neither alive nor dead. Mina's fresh blood is still on his lips. We must hurry. Hand me the wooden stake and the hammer.

Renfield: Not so fast, Doctor!

Count Dracula meets a painful death at the end of the movie. In real life, Bela Lugosi didn't do so well, either. He struggled for the rest of his life to land good roles. Why? That accent. And Lugosi refused the one good, non-speaking role he was offered—the monster in *Frankenstein*.

Narrator 1: The patient, Renfield, stands in the shadows. He aims a pistol at the men.

Seward: Renfield! What are you doing here?

Renfield: The Master knew you would come. He called me here to protect him.

Seward: So that's why you've acted this way. Dracula is controlling your mind. Don't you understand? He's evil! He will destroy your soul!

Renfield: The last bit of sunlight will be gone in a few minutes. Then the Master will rise. You can talk about it with him.

Van Helsing *(whispering)*: He's right. We must hurry. This is our only chance.

Narrator 2: Harker tackles Renfield and takes the gun. At that moment, Dracula begins to wake up.

Harker: Do it now, Professor, while he is still weak from sleep!

Narrator 1: Professor Van Helsing pounds the stake into Dracula's heart. A terrible scream fills the air. Blood bubbles out of the vampire's mouth. Moments later, Dracula's entire body turns into sand, then disappears.

Van Helsing: It is over, gentlemen. The curse is lifted.

Narrator 2: They quickly return to check on Mina.

Seward: Mina was barely alive this morning, but she seems better already. And the wounds on her neck are gone!

Mina: Jonathan, is that you? You're alive!

Harker: It's all over, Mina. We're together now. And we are all free of the vampire's curse.

Van Helsing: Let's hope you are right.

About the Author

Bram Stoker was born in Dublin, Ireland, in 1847. He began his writing career as a drama critic for a newspaper. Soon, he was writing other kinds of articles and stories.

In 1890, Stoker got the idea for a book about a bloodsucking monster. He went to libraries and read everything he could find about vampires. He combined stories from Greece, South America, and Eastern Europe.

Stoker's novel, *Dracula*, soon became popular all over Europe and the United States. Dozens of horror films have been based on his Transylvanian vampire. And Dracula has become one of the most famous monsters in the world.

Romeo and Juliet

**Illustrations
Lamberto Alvarez**

Romeo and Juliet

**Based on the classic play
by William Shakespeare**

SCHOLASTIC INC.
New York   Toronto   London   Auckland   Sydney
Mexico City   New Delhi   Hong Kong   Buenos Aires

Characters

THE CAPULETS
Juliet
Lady Capulet, Juliet's mother
Capulet, Juliet's father
Tybalt, Juliet's cousin

THE MONTAGUES
Romeo
Benvolio, Romeo's cousin
Montague, Romeo's father

OTHERS
Narrator
Balthasar, Romeo's servant
Nurse, Juliet's nurse
Friar Laurence, a priest
Mercutio, Romeo's friend
Prince of Verona
Paris, a nobleman who wants to marry Juliet
Friar John, a priest
Guard

Scene 1

Narrator: The play takes place in the early 1500s, in Verona, a city in Italy. There, two families are fighting—the Capulets and the Montagues. When the play begins, Romeo, a Montague, is with his cousin Benvolio. Romeo has just been rejected by a girl named Rosaline. Benvolio is trying to cheer him up.

Benvolio: Forget about Rosaline. Let's go to the Capulets' costume party tonight. You'll meet someone else.

Romeo: I can't go to the Capulets' house. I am a Montague. We are enemies.

Benvolio: Enough of your father's feud! We'll wear masks. No one will know who we

are. And if you go, you might catch a glimpse of Rosaline.

Narrator: Meanwhile, in the Capulet house, Juliet and her nurse listen to Lady Capulet.

Lady Capulet: Nurse, you know my daughter is almost 14.

Nurse: Yes—in a couple of weeks.

Lady Capulet: So it's time she married. Juliet, what do you think of that?

Juliet: I never dreamed of such an honor.

Lady Capulet: The good man Paris now seeks your hand. He'll be at the party tonight. Read his face like a diary and tell me if you like what's written there.

Juliet: I'll try to see what you want me to.

Lady Capulet tells Juliet to read Paris's face "like a diary." What does she mean?

Scene 2

Narrator: It's the night of the Capulets' party. Romeo, Benvolio, and Mercutio enter wearing masks.

Capulet: Welcome! I hope you'll all dance!

Narrator: Romeo notices Juliet.

Romeo *(to Benvolio)*: Who is that lady? I've never seen such beauty. She is so radiant that she teaches torches how to shine.

Narrator: At the same time, Tybalt, who is a member of the Capulet family, notices Romeo. He draws his sword.

Tybalt: That's the voice of a Montague. How dare he come here!

Capulet: What's wrong? Put down your sword!

Tybalt: Uncle, that Montague is our enemy!

Capulet: Don't create a scene tonight. It's only young Romeo.

Tybalt: All right, but I'll take care of him later.

Narrator: At the same time, Romeo approaches Juliet.

Romeo: We have not been introduced. But would you like to dance?

Juliet: I would.

Narrator: Romeo kisses Juliet's hand. They dance dreamily a few moments. In fact, they are falling in love. Then Juliet's nurse interrupts.

Nurse: Juliet, your mother wants a word with you.

Narrator: Juliet leaves.

Romeo *(to Nurse)*: Who is her mother?

Nurse: The lady of the house.

Romeo: So that girl is a Capulet? Oh, no!

Benvolio: We'd better go.

Narrator: Romeo and Benvolio leave. Nurse rejoins Juliet.

Juliet: Who was that boy? I hope he's not married!

Nurse: He's Romeo, the only son of your father's worst enemy.

Juliet: My only hate is now my only love!

What does Juliet mean when she says that Romeo is her "only hate" and her "only love"?

Scene 3

Narrator: The next night, Romeo walks sadly around the Capulets' orchard.

Romeo: I should go home, but I can't take my body where my heart won't follow.

Narrator: A figure appears in a window above. Romeo sees that it is Juliet.

Romeo (*to himself*): Wait! What light is that in the window? It is Juliet, more beautiful than the sun!

Narrator: Juliet is thinking about Romeo. She imagines she is speaking with him. She doesn't know that he is outside and can hear her.

Juliet: Oh, Romeo! Why are you called Romeo? It's only your name that is my enemy. And a rose by any other name would smell as sweet. Romeo, give up your name for me!

Romeo: Call me your love, and I won't be Romeo anymore!

Juliet (*surprised*): Who's there?

Narrator: Juliet walks out onto her balcony. She sees Romeo on the ground below.

Romeo: I'd tell you my name—if I didn't hate it so much.

Juliet: Romeo? What are you doing here? The guards will kill you!

Romeo: It's love that brought me here. I have to know if you love me, too. Let them kill me. It would be worth it to hear you say you love me.

Juliet: I have to go. My nurse is coming! If you mean what you say, let me know tomorrow. I'll send someone to set a wedding

date. If you agree to a time and place, I'll know you are serious.

Romeo: Send someone at nine o'clock. I'll be waiting.

Juliet: It seems like twenty years until then. Parting is such sweet sorrow. Let us say good night until tomorrow.

Juliet says that "a rose by any other name would smell as sweet." What is she saying about the fact that Romeo's last name is Montague?

Scene 4

Narrator: Early the next morning, Romeo visits Friar Laurence at the church.

Friar Laurence: Why are you up so early?

Romeo: I'm in love with Juliet of the Capulets. She loves me too. Can you marry us today?

Friar Laurence: Weren't you in love with Rosaline just a few days ago?

Romeo: This is completely different.

Friar Laurence: I knew your love for Rosaline wasn't real. Now, your love for Juliet may bring peace to the war between your families. I'll help, but we must be careful. Those who are hasty often stumble.

Scene 5

Narrator: Later that day, Mercutio and Benvolio walk down the street.

Mercutio: Where was Romeo last night?

Benvolio: His father said he was out all night. *(He pauses.)* You know, Tybalt sent a letter challenging him to a duel.

Mercutio: Romeo is in no state to fight Tybalt. He's completely lovesick, and Tybalt is a fierce fighter!

Narrator: Romeo walks up.

Mercutio: Where were you last night?

Romeo: I had some business.

Narrator: Just then, Juliet's nurse walks up.

Nurse: I'm looking for young Romeo.

Romeo: I am Romeo.

Nurse: I must speak with you in private.

Benvolio: The old lady's asking him out!

Narrator: Mercutio and Benvolio leave.

Nurse: Juliet wants to know if you were telling your true feelings last night.

Romeo: I give you my word. I have arranged a wedding in Friar Laurence's cell this afternoon.

Nurse: You look as lovesick as Juliet. I'll tell her about your plan.

Narrator: Meanwhile, Juliet waits for her nurse.

Juliet: She left three hours ago! Talk about slow! I think some old folks practice being dead before they die!

Narrator: The nurse comes in.

Juliet: What did Romeo say?

Nurse: I'm so tired from the walk. Let me catch my breath.

Juliet: You have the breath to say you're tired. Don't you have the breath to tell me yes or no? Tell me now!

Nurse: The wedding's on. Now eat your lunch. Then we'll be on our way to Friar Laurence.

Narrator: Juliet and her nurse go to see Friar Laurence. Romeo is waiting. Friar Laurence conducts the wedding ceremony.

Do you think this marriage will bring peace to the Montagues and Capulets, as Friar Laurence hopes it will?

Scene 6

Narrator: That same afternoon, Romeo's friends Benvolio and Mercutio are talking in the street. Tybalt and several other Capulet men approach.

Tybalt: I'd like a word with one of you.

Mercutio: Just a word? Not a word and a fight?

Tybalt: I'll fight if you give me a reason. Mercutio, you're a part of Romeo's band, aren't you?

Mercutio: Band? Do you mistake us for musicians? Well, here's my instrument. *(He draws his sword.)* And it will make you dance!

Narrator: Just then Romeo appears.

Tybalt *(drawing his sword)*: Peace to you, Mercutio. Here's the man I hate.

Romeo: Tybalt, there's good reason for us not to fight. Your name is now as dear to me as my own.

Tybalt: You're a villain! Draw your sword!

Mercutio: Tybalt, you can't talk to my friend Romeo like that!

Narrator: Tybalt and Mercutio fight.

Romeo: Tybalt! Mercutio! Stop!

Narrator: Tybalt stabs Mercutio and runs away.

Mercutio: He stabbed me! They've made worm's meat out of me. Help me, Benvolio!

Narrator: Benvolio carries Mercutio to a nearby house for help. He soon comes back.

Benvolio *(to Romeo)*: Mercutio is dead!

Narrator: Just then, Tybalt returns.

Romeo: Tybalt, draw your sword! You killed my friend. Now one of us will join him!

Tybalt: I'm afraid it will have to be you!

Narrator: Tybalt and Romeo fight. Tybalt falls dead at Romeo's feet.

Benvolio: Romeo, get out of here fast! The Prince will surely sentence you to death.

Narrator: Romeo flees as a crowd gathers. The Prince, Montague, Lady Montague, Capulet, and Lady Capulet are there.

Prince: Benvolio, how did this begin?

Benvolio: Tybalt killed Mercutio, and Romeo killed Tybalt in revenge.

Lady Capulet: Romeo must pay with his life.

Montague: No! Romeo does not deserve to die. He was only getting revenge for his friend's death.

Prince: I sentence Romeo to exile. He must leave Verona forever. And if he ever comes back, he will be killed.

Narrator: Juliet is in her chamber. Her nurse bursts in.

Juliet: What news do you have of Romeo?

Nurse *(upset)*: He's dead! He's dead!

Juliet *(alarmed)*: What are you saying?

Nurse: I saw it with my own eyes—a gaping wound in Tybalt's chest!

Juliet: What? Are you saying that Romeo and Tybalt are both dead?

Nurse: Tybalt is dead, and Romeo is exiled. Romeo killed Tybalt.

Juliet: Romeo killed my cousin? How can that be?

Nurse: There's no honesty in men.

Juliet: I can't curse the husband I vowed to love only three hours ago. Romeo is good. It must be that if Romeo had not killed Tybalt, Tybalt would have killed him. Oh, I feel better already. My husband, who would have been killed by my cousin, is alive. If only he were not exiled! I'll never see him again, will I?

Nurse: I happen to know that he's hiding in Friar Laurence's cell.

Juliet: Oh, please find him, Nurse. And give him this ring.

How does Juliet feel about Romeo killing her cousin Tybalt?

Scene 8

Narrator: Meanwhile, Romeo seeks the help of Friar Laurence in the monastery.

Romeo: How can I live without Juliet? Every cat, dog, and mouse is free to look at her, and I am not. The Prince killed me with that word, *exile*.

Narrator: There is a knock at the door. Juliet's nurse enters.

Romeo: Nurse, how is Juliet? Does she think I'm nothing but a murderer?

Nurse: She cries all the time—sometimes for Tybalt, sometimes for you.

Romeo (*pulling out a dagger*): I'll kill myself!

Friar Laurence: Stop! If you kill yourself, Juliet will be destroyed, too. Now you and Juliet are both alive, and tonight you can be together. Go and comfort her. Just be sure to leave Verona before daybreak. While you're in exile, you can beg pardon from the Prince.

Nurse: Here is a ring Juliet asked me to give you, Romeo. I'll go tell her that you are coming tonight.

Narrator: Back at the Capulet house, Capulet and Lady Capulet sit with Paris. None of them know that Juliet has married Romeo.

Capulet: Juliet dearly loved her cousin Tybalt. She is so sick with grief that she won't come down tonight.

Paris: I understand. A time of tragedy is not a time to fall in love.

Lady Capulet: I'll talk to her tomorrow.

Capulet: I think she will agree to marry you. Let's set the wedding date for Thursday.

Paris: I wish tomorrow were Thursday!

Scene 9

Narrator: The next morning at dawn, Romeo and Juliet stand on her balcony. He is preparing to leave.

Juliet: Tell me that it's not morning.

Romeo: I'll say that daylight is moonlight, Juliet. I will say anything to make you happy.

Juliet: Then say that you will stay.

Romeo: I will stay and die, or leave and live. Whatever you want.

Juliet: No, you must go. It *is* morning. They will be looking for you.

Nurse *(entering)*: Juliet, your mother is coming!

Juliet *(to Romeo)*: Farewell! Will I ever see you again?

Romeo: Our time apart will make our future together more sweet.

Narrator: Romeo climbs down from the balcony as Lady Capulet comes into Juliet's room.

Lady Capulet: Juliet, you look pale. Are you still weeping for your cousin's death? Tears will not bring him back.

Juliet: I can't stop crying.

Lady Capulet: I'm sure you grieve also because that murderous Romeo is still alive.

Juliet: It's true that Romeo grieves my heart.

Lady Capulet: But listen now. I have some happy news. On Thursday morning, you'll marry Paris at Saint Peter's Church!

Juliet: I don't want to get married yet! And if I did, well, I'd sooner marry Romeo, whom you hate, than Paris!

Lady Capulet (*shocked*): Here comes your father. Tell him that yourself.

Capulet *(entering)*: What's wrong, Juliet? Still crying? Haven't you heard the news?

Lady Capulet: She's heard, but she'll have none of it.

Capulet: You're not happy that I've found you a good husband?

Juliet: No!

Capulet *(angry)*: Listen, Juliet. You'll be married Thursday in Saint Peter's Church—even if I have to drag you there!

Juliet: Oh, Mother, help me! Delay this marriage by a month—or even a week!

Lady Capulet: I've had enough of this!

Narrator: Juliet's parents leave.

Juliet: Oh, Nurse! How can I marry Paris when Romeo is still alive?

Nurse: Romeo is as good as dead. It's best you marry Paris.

Juliet: You really think so?

Nurse: With all my soul!

Juliet *(lying)*: You're right. Please go tell my mother I have gone to Friar Laurence. I need to confess that I have displeased my father.

Nurse *(leaving)*: I will.

Juliet: You old witch! I'll never trust you again. I'll ask the Friar for a solution. If he does not have one, I am ready to die!

Why doesn't Juliet just tell her parents that she is already married?

Scene 10

Narrator: Friar Laurence is in his cell, talking with Paris.

Friar Laurence: On Thursday? That is very soon. What does Juliet say?

Paris: She weeps and weeps for Tybalt's death, so I don't dare talk of love. Her father thinks that the sooner we marry, the sooner she'll recover from her grief.

Narrator: Just then, Juliet enters.

Paris: Hello, my wife.

Juliet: I'm not your wife yet!

Paris: Have you come to make confession?

Juliet: That's none of your business. *(to Friar Laurence)* Do you have a moment?

Friar Laurence: I do. Please excuse us, sir.

Paris *(leaving)*: Until Thursday morning, Juliet.

Juliet: Friar, what should I do? My heart is joined to Romeo's. If I'm forced to marry someone else—I'd rather die!

Friar Laurence: You're not afraid of death? Then maybe you are brave enough to *almost* die.

Juliet: I'd jump off a tower to avoid marrying Paris. I would hide in a grave to stay true to Romeo.

Friar Laurence *(handing her a small bottle)*: If that is true, I have a solution. Go home. Tell your parents you'll marry Paris. On Wednesday night, drink the potion in this bottle. It will make you appear to be dead for 42 hours. They'll bury you in the family tomb. When you wake up, Romeo will be there to take you to Mantua where he is living.

Juliet: Thank you! I will not give in to fear.

Friar Laurence: I'll have Friar John carry a letter to Romeo, explaining everything.

Narrator: The night before the wedding, Juliet's mother and nurse try to help her with her jewelry and dress.

Juliet: Please leave me alone tonight. I'd like to say my prayers.

Narrator: They leave.

Juliet (*holding up the bottle*): What if this mixture fails in some way? What if it doesn't work, and I have to get married tomorrow? Or what if it kills me? Or what if I wake up before Romeo comes to get me? I could suffocate in the tomb alongside Tybalt.

Narrator: The next morning. Capulet sends the nurse up to fetch Juliet.

Nurse: Wake up! Wake up! It's your wedding day! Wake up!

Narrator: She pulls open the bed-curtains.

Nurse: You slug-a-bed! Get up now! Why are you wearing yesterday's clothes? *(She checks Juliet's pulse.)* Oh, no! No! She's dead!

Narrator: Lady Capulet enters the room.

Lady Capulet: What's all the noise about?

Nurse: Our sweet Juliet is dead! What a horrible day this is!

Lady Capulet: My only child? My life? *(She calls out.)* Help!

Narrator: Capulet comes in.

Capulet: Get Juliet up. The groom is here.

Lady Capulet *(crying)*: Our child has already married Death.

Narrator: Capulet checks Juliet's pulse. He finds none. He is speechless with shock. Then Friar Laurence and Paris come in.

Friar Laurence: Is the bride ready to go to church?

Lady Capulet: Ready to go, but never to return. My child is dead.

Paris *(upset)*: How cruel! I have been wronged by death.

Capulet: The wedding has become a funeral. The bridal flowers will decorate the tomb.

What are Juliet's fears as she prepares to drink from the bottle?

Scene 12

Narrator: In his house in Mantua, Romeo wakes up from a troubled sleep.

Romeo: How strange. I dreamed that Juliet came and found me dead. She kissed me, and I came back to life.

Narrator: Romeo's servant, Balthasar, comes in.

Romeo: Balthasar, what news is there from Verona? How is Juliet? If she is well, then nothing can be bad.

Balthasar: I am sorry to report that she is dead. Juliet sleeps in the Capulet tomb.

Romeo: Oh, it cannot be! Get my horses! I'm going to her grave! Why didn't the friar send word of this?

Balthasar: Please slow down. You're in shock.

Narrator: Romeo buys some poison. Then he hurries toward the Capulet tomb.

Romeo: I'll lie with Juliet tonight.

Narrator: Meanwhile, Friar John arrives back at Friar Laurence's cell.

Friar Laurence: Friar John, welcome back from Mantua. What did Romeo say about our plan?

Friar John: I never had a chance to see him.

Friar Laurence: Why not?

Friar John: Another friar went to Mantua with me. He had been taking care of the sick. The officials feared that he'd spread the illness. We were not allowed to enter the city.

Friar Laurence: Then who took my letter to Romeo?

Friar John: I could get no one to take it to him. They were all afraid of the illness.

Friar Laurence: Oh, no! Juliet will wake within three hours, and Romeo won't be there to rescue her from the tomb! Friar John, get me a crowbar quickly!

Narrator: Friar John gets the crowbar.

Friar Laurence: I'll bring Juliet back here and send again for Romeo.

Why is it important that someone rescue Juliet from the tomb?

Scene 13

Narrator: Meanwhile, Paris goes to the cemetery to mourn for Juliet. He begins scattering flowers on the Capulet tomb. Then he hears footsteps.

Paris: Who's that?

Narrator: Paris sees Romeo and Balthasar with a torch, an ax, and a crowbar. He hides so he can watch them.

Romeo: Balthasar, give me the tools. Tomorrow, give this letter to my father. I am opening the tomb to see my lady's face once more. Now, go away. If you return, I'll kill you.

Balthasar: I will be gone, sir.

Narrator: Balthasar is worried, but he leaves. Then Paris comes out of the shadows.

Paris *(to himself)*: That is Romeo, who killed Juliet's cousin. And her grief then caused her to die. He should be in exile. *(He shouts.)* Stop, you villain Montague! I have caught you in Verona, so you must die! Your funeral is long overdue.

Romeo: Leave me alone! I am armed against myself, and I might do you harm. I am a desperate man.

Paris: I hereby arrest you.

Romeo: You're forcing me to kill you!

Narrator: They fight, and Paris falls.

Paris: I am killed! Please bury me with Juliet!

Romeo: Believe me, I will.

Narrator: Romeo opens the tomb and lays Paris in it.

Romeo: Here lies Juliet, and there lies Tybalt. Forgive me, Tybalt. And Juliet, even death

could not conquer your beauty. How can you still glow with life in this dark tomb? Now I will rest with you forever. I drink this to you, my sweet!

Narrator: Romeo drinks the poison and dies. Soon, Juliet wakes up.

Juliet: It worked. I'm where the friar said I'd be. But where is Romeo?

Narrator: She sees Romeo lying dead. She is horrified. She takes the bottle and tries to drink from it. It is empty.

Juliet: Romeo, how could you take all that poison and leave none for me? Perhaps enough poison still clings to your lips.

Narrator: She kisses him.

Juliet: Oh, your lips are still warm! I'll be quick to join you.

Narrator: Juliet stabs herself with Romeo's dagger.

Juliet *(falling)*: Oh, happy dagger, let me die!

47

Narrator: Soon, guards come and discover the bodies. They capture Friar Laurence and Balthasar. Then the guards summon the Prince, the Montagues, and the Capulets.

Prince: What brings us here at this early hour?

Guard: Paris is slain, and Romeo is dead. Juliet, who has been dead two days, lies newly killed. And we have caught a friar and Romeo's man, Balthasar, both carrying tools to open a tomb.

Capulet: Look how our poor daughter bleeds!

Montague: My son is dead! What more could go wrong?

Prince: This must be cleared up.

Narrator: Friar Laurence explains all he knows of the story, beginning with the wedding of Romeo and Juliet.

Prince: Friar, we know you to be an honest man. But we need proof.

Balthasar: Romeo gave me this letter to give to his father.

Prince *(inspecting the letter)*: The letter confirms what the friar said. Romeo wrote that he bought a poison so that he might die here and be buried with Juliet. Capulet, Montague, see what your feuding has caused. Everyone has been punished. Death is the only winner.

Capulet *(crying)*: Oh, Montague, give me your hand. Since I cannot offer my daughter in marriage to your son, this is the best I can do.

Montague *(shaking Capulet's hand)*: I will raise a gold statue of Juliet, so all Verona will remember her.

Prince: This is a sad peace. There has never been a story more full of woe than this tale of Juliet and her Romeo.

Earlier in the play, Friar Laurence warns Romeo, "Those who are hasty often stumble." Do you think that the actions of Romeo and Juliet prove or disprove this idea?

About the Author

William Shakespeare was born in England in 1564. When he was 18, he married a woman named Ann Hathaway. Shakespeare supported his family by writing, acting, and directing. His first play was produced in 1592, when he was 28 years old.

Romeo and Juliet is now about 400 years old. But like most of Shakespeare's work, it is still popular. The movie *Romeo + Juliet,* starring Claire Danes and Leonardo DiCaprio, was a modern retelling of Shakespeare's play. And the movie *Shakespeare in Love* imagined what Shakespeare's life was like while he was writing *Romeo and Juliet.*